THIS BOOK BELONGS TO...

....

101 USES FOR A SKATEBOARD

WRITTEN AND ILLUSTRATED
BY ADAM McEVOY

Dedicated to Mumma Wells.

RED FEZ
BOOKS
PUBLISHING WORDS & PICTURES

101 USES FOR A SKATEBOARD?
WHATEVER CAN THEY BE?
TAKE A LOOK,
INSIDE THIS BOOK,
101 USES FOR A
ATEBOARD?
READ ME.
101 USES FOR A
SKATEBOA
AND
YOU WILL PLAINLY SEE!!

WHEN DIGGING UP TREASURE,

IT'S USEFUL AS A SPADE,

OR YOU CAN WEAR IT AS A SCARF, IF YOUR OLD ONE'S OVER-FRAYED...

WHEN FIGHTING OFF INJUSTICE, IT'S USEFUL AS A **SIGN,**

OR A RATHER FANCY CHEESE BOARD FOR CAMEMBERT AND **WINE**!!

IF AN ELEPHANT IS IN A RUSH, THEY MAKE GREAT ROLLER- SKATES,

OR.. DOUBLE UP AS DISHES,

IF YOU'VE ONLY DIRTY PLATES!!

CONVENIENT
AS A SPOON,
FOR WHEN
YOU STIR
YOUR **TEAS**,

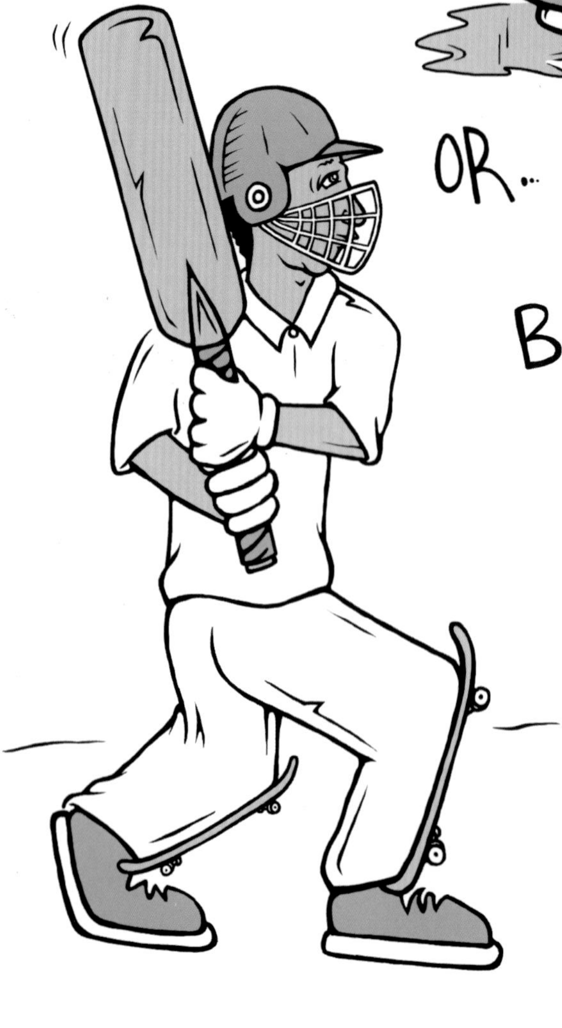

OR...

WHEN
BATTING DURING
CRICKET,
WEAR TWO
UPON YOUR
KNEES!!

WEAR THEM AS GLASSES, TO PROTECT YOU FROM THE SUN, OR..
A SUBSTITUTE FOR A WALRUS TUSK... IF IT'S MISSING ONE!!

YOUNG MILLIE AT THE PLAYGROUND, USES IT AS A SWING...
AND
IF YOU BEND IT WISELY, IT'S A GIANT'S WEDDING RING!

WHEN GOING INTO BATTLE, IT BECOMES A TRUSTY SHIELD...

OR...

USE IT AS A SCARECROW, TO PROTECT YOUR FIELD!!

STRAP UP, GET ON BOARD THE FRANTIC ROLLER-COASTER OR IF YOU'RE HUNGRY SLIP TWO INSIDE, YOUR FANCY RETRO TOASTER!!

THE CONCAVE ONES MAKE BIRD BATHS, WHERE BIRDS CAN GET ALL MATEY...

BIG TONY'S IS A DARTBOARD, AND HE ALWAYS SCORES ONE HUNDRED AND... EIGHTY!!

IT'S BETTER THAN ANY SUSHI..
YOU CAN EAT IT RAW..
OR...
A REPLACEMENT FOR A CROCODILE... MISSING IT'S UPPER JAW!!

IF YOU'RE FOND OF MAGIC YOU CAN PULL IT FROM A HAT....

AND WHEN YOU'RE PLAYING BASEBALL, YOU CAN SWING ONE AS A BAT!!

USE IT AS A SCRATCHER, WHEN YOU'VE GOT AN ITCHY BACK,

OR.. WEAR ONE AS A TIE AND YOU'LL NEVER GET THE SACK!!

WHEN YOU WANT TO KEEP THE FIZZ IN, IT CAN BE A BOTTLE TOP,

OR A SOLID WOODEN STICK FOR YOUR FAVOURITE ICEY- POP!!

A PROFESSIONAL SNOOKER TABLE,

WITH BALLS THAT YOU CAN SINK, OR COOLING AS A FAN, WHEN YOU HAVE'NT GOT A DRINK!!

THE ANTLERS OF A GRUMPY STAG, WHO REALLY LIKES TO MOAN, OR THE HANDLE AND RECIEVER, OF AN OLD SKOOL TELE-PHONE!!

USE ONE AS A LOUNGER,

IF YOU'RE NOT TOO FOND OF SAND,

OR... TO OPEN UP A METAL TIN,

PEACHES

IF YOUR FOOD IS CANNED!!

SEE THEM AT THE CIRCUS, WHEN JUGGLED BY A CLOWN,

AND...

IF BALLANCED PRECISELY, YOUR TOTEM WON'T FALL DOWN!!

EARS FOR A BUNNY, WHO LOVES TO HOP AND JUMP,

OR...

SNAP ONE CLEAN IN HALF, TO FORM A CAMEL'S HUMP!!

THE TRUSTY LEG OF A PIRATE, WHO'S DRUNKEN ALL THE RUM

OR..

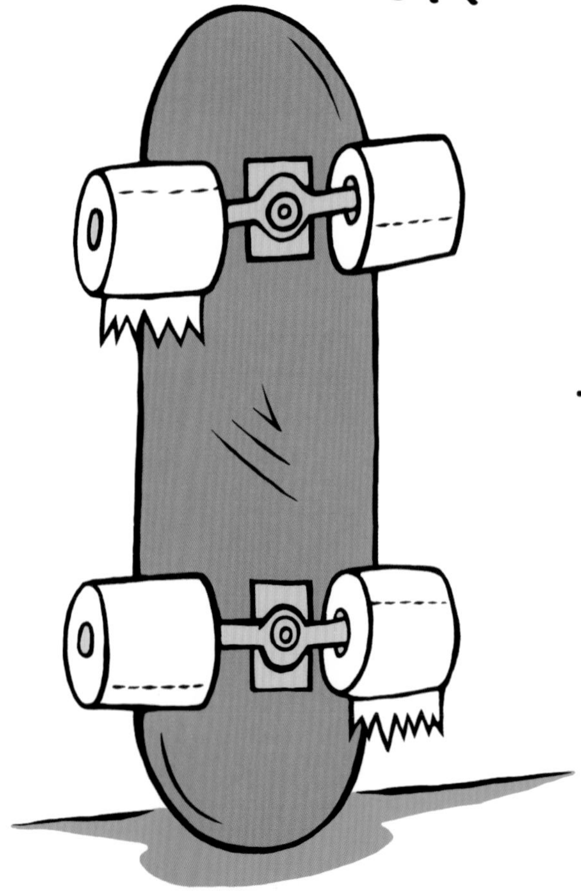

REPLACE YOUR WHEELS WITH TOILET ROLLS, FOR USE UPON YOUR UMM...

AN EFFICIENT BUZZING BEEHIVE, FOR A SWARM OF WORKER **BEES,** OR..

AN AERODYNAMIC FRISBEE, YOU CAN THROW AND CATCH WITH EASE!!

THE BAMBOO ONES MAKE A

SCRUMPTIOUS PANDA

DINNER, OR.. UTILIZE WITH YOUR KARATE KICKS, SO YOU'LL ALWAYS BE A WINNER !!

A FETCHING BIKINI TOP, WHEN BATHING AT THE **BEACH,** OR..

AN EDUCATIONAL BLACKBOARD, FOR PROFESSOR BIMMS TO TEACH!!

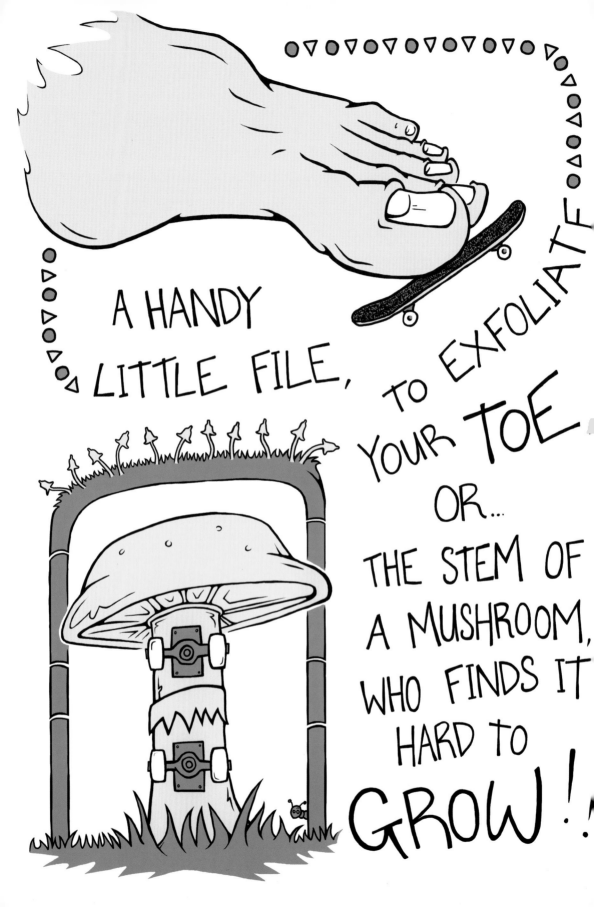

WHEN OFF CAMPING...

IT FORMS A VERY COMFY TENT, OR GRANDAD'S FAVOURITE WALKING STICK, BECAUSE HIS BACK IS BENT...

WHEN SEARCHING FOR A FUGITIVE, IT'LL HELP A HELICOPTER RUN..

OR WHEN FIGHTING MARTIANS IN OUTER SPACE, IT TRANSFORMS INTO A GUN!!

LOTS AND LOTS OF FUN...

WHEN YOU FLY IT AS A KITE!!

PLUS...

YOU'LL ALWAYS WIN AT CHESS.

WHEN THE MOVE IS RIGHT!

A BUSKER'S SLICK GUITAR, WHEN HE WANTS TO SING AND PLAY,

OR.. A CALM RELAXING SEAT,

TO WATCH THE END OF DAY?!

NOPE......
A HUNDRED AND ONE....
USE IT AS A SKATEBOARD,
AND RIDE IT UP THE WALL!!

101 USES FOR A SKATEBOARD

WRITTEN AND ILLUSTRATED BY ADAM McEVOY

THANKS TO...

Josh, Jak, Jerry, Joan, Iman, Jono, Tony, Wombat, Si and Millie

ABOUT THE AUTHOR/ILLUSTRATOR...

Adam McEvoy has been a designer within the skateboard industry for over 20 years.
His artwork has been collected and sold worldwide.
Adam is also a proud father and has told his daughter 1000s of stories over the years.
"101 Uses for a Skateboard" is Adam's first publication which combines 4 great passions in his life, fatherhood, drawing, skateboarding and imagination.